RUSS SHIPTONS Rock & Pop Guitar Songbook 1

Contents

Note: The songs in this book are taken from "Russ Shiptons Rock & Pop Guitar" Coursebooks 1 & 2. The Coursebooks and matching cassettes include the analysis and demonstration of chords, rhythm patterns and techniques needed to play the accompaniments effectively (see back cover)

First Published 1986
© International Music Publications

Exclusive Distributors
International Music Publications
Southend Road, Woodford Green,
Essex IG8 8HN, England.

SATISFACTION (I Can't Get No)

Words and Music by
MICK JAGGER and KEITH RICHARD

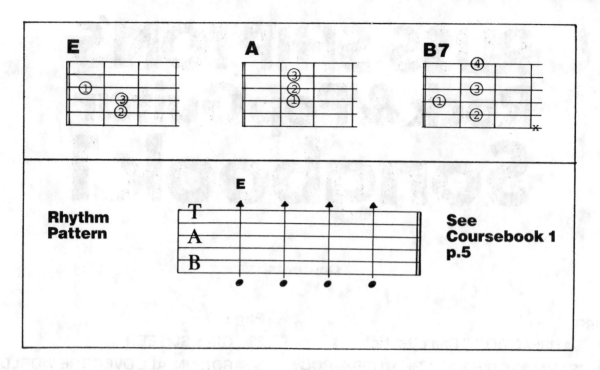

CHORUS

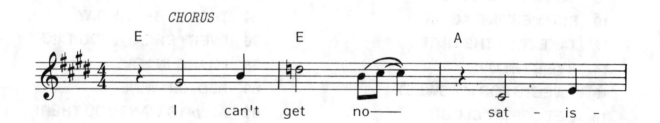

I can't get no—— sat - is -

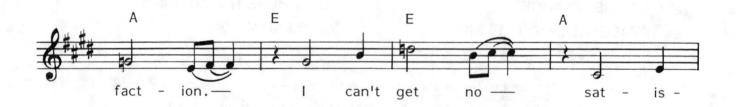

fact - ion.—— I can't get no —— sat - is -

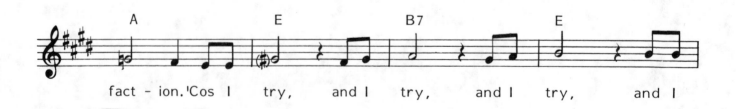

fact - ion.'Cos I try, and I try, and I try, and I

try.—— I can't get no, I can't get no. . .

Westminster Music Ltd, 19/20 Poland Street, London W1V 3DD

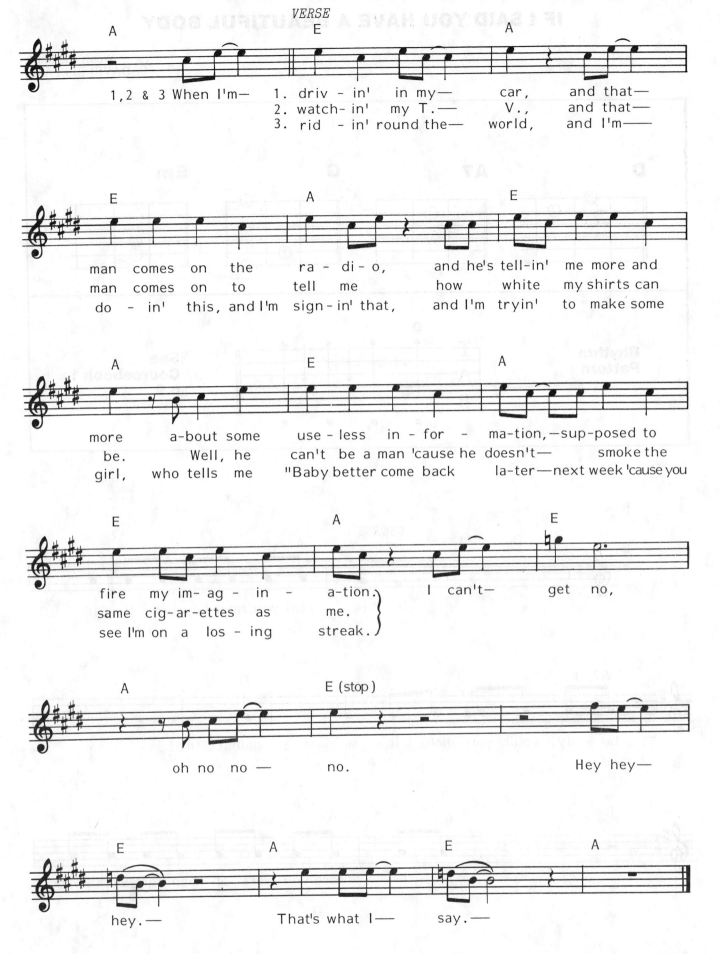

1,2 & 3 When I'm— 1. driv-in' in my— car, and that—
2. watch-in' my T.— V., and that—
3. rid-in' round the— world, and I'm——

man comes on the ra-di-o, and he's tell-in' me more and
man comes on to tell me how white my shirts can
do-in' this, and I'm sign-in' that, and I'm tryin' to make some

more a-bout some use-less in-for-ma-tion,—sup-posed to
be. Well, he can't be a man 'cause he doesn't— smoke the
girl, who tells me "Baby better come back la-ter—next week 'cause you

fire my im-ag-in-a-tion.} I can't— get no,
same cig-ar-ettes as me.}
see I'm on a los-ing streak.}

oh no no— no. Hey hey—

hey.— That's what I— say.—

IF I SAID YOU HAVE A BEAUTIFUL BODY

Words and Music
by DAVID BELLAMY

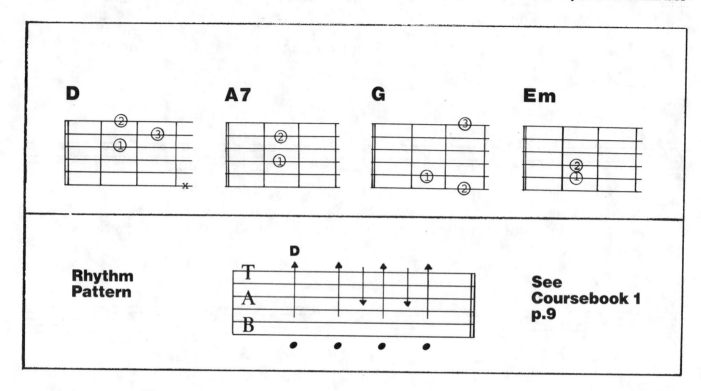

CHORUS

If I said you have a beau-ti-ful bo - dy, would you hold it a - gainst me?

If I swore you were an an - gel, would you

treat me like the dev - il to - night? ——

HELLO MARYLOU (GOODBYE HEART)

Words and Music
by GENE PITNEY

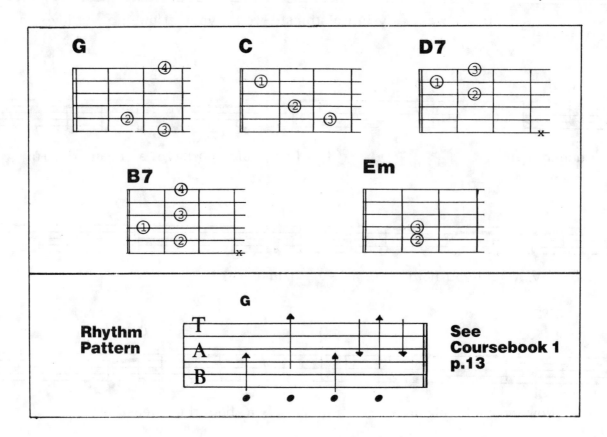

Rhythm Pattern   **See Coursebook 1 p.13**

CHORUS

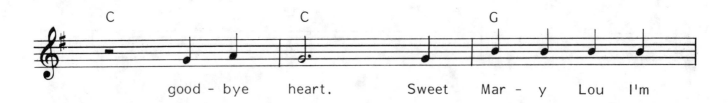

I said "Hel - lo, Mar - y Lou,

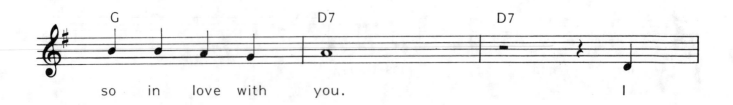

good - bye heart. Sweet Mar - y Lou I'm

so in love with you.   I

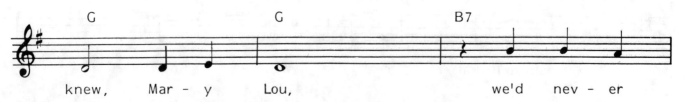

knew, Mar - y Lou,   we'd nev - er

part, so hel - lo Mar - y Lou, good-bye heart."

VERSE

1. You passed me by one sun - ny day, ——
2. I saw your lips, I heard your voice, —— Be-

Flashed those big brown eyes my way, and oo I want - ed
lieve me I just had no choice, wild hors - es could - n't

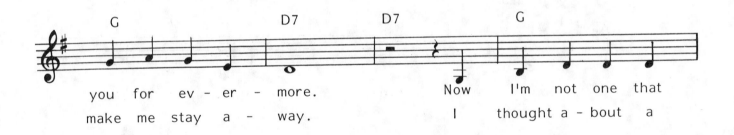

you for ev - er - more. Now I'm not one that
make me stay a - way. I thought a - bout a

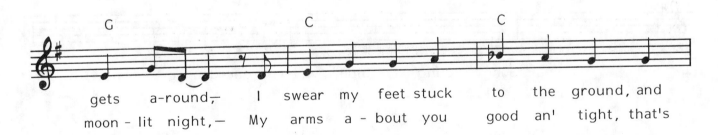

gets a-round, I swear my feet stuck to the ground, and
moon - lit night, — My arms a - bout you good an' tight, that's

though I nev - er did meet you be - fore.
all I had to see for me to stay.

SONG SUNG BLUE

Words and Music
by NEIL DIAMOND

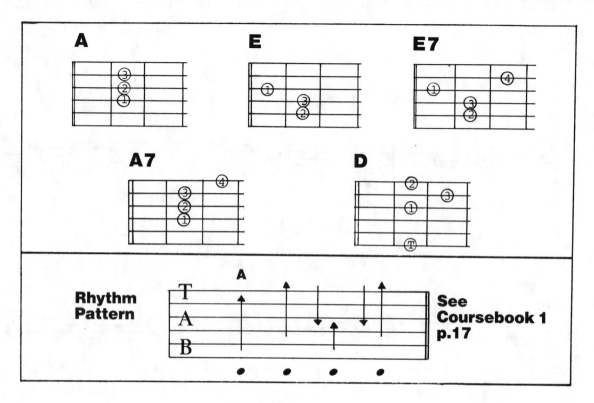

Song sung blue, ev-ery-bo-dy knows one.

Song sung blue, ev-ery gar-den grows one.

Me and you are sub-ject to the

blues now and then, But when you take the blues and make a

song, you sing them out a-gain,— Sing them

VERSE 2

out a-gain.————— Song sung blue, weep-in' like a

wil-low.— Song sung blue, sleep-in' on my

pil-low. Fun-ny— thing, but you can sing it with a

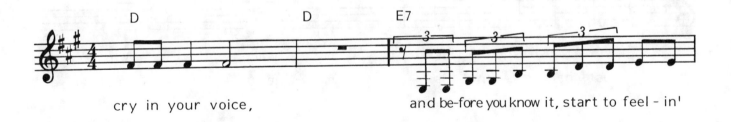

cry in your voice, and be-fore you know it, start to feel-in'

good. You sim-ply got no choice.—

SUMMERTIME AGAIN

Words and Music
by RUSS SHIPTON

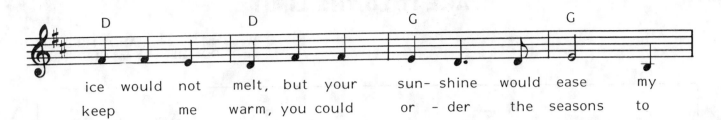

ice would not melt, but your sun- shine would ease my

keep me warm, you could or - der the seasons to

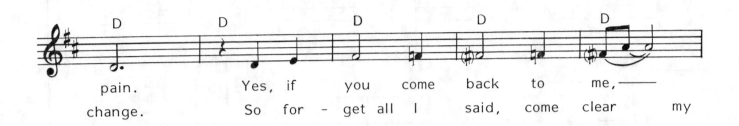

pain. Yes, if you come back to me,——

change. So for - get all I said, come clear my

it would be sum-mer— time a - gain.)

head, make it sum-mer— time a - gain.)

CHORUS

Sum-mer— time a - gain.—— Sum-mer—

time a - gain.———————— Oh, if you walked through that

door, my love, you'd stop this win - ter rain.

TAKE IT TO THE LIMIT

Words and Music by RANDY MEISNER,
DON HENLEY and GLEN FREY

BYE BYE LOVE

Words and Music by
FELICE BRYANT and BOUDLEAUX BRYANT

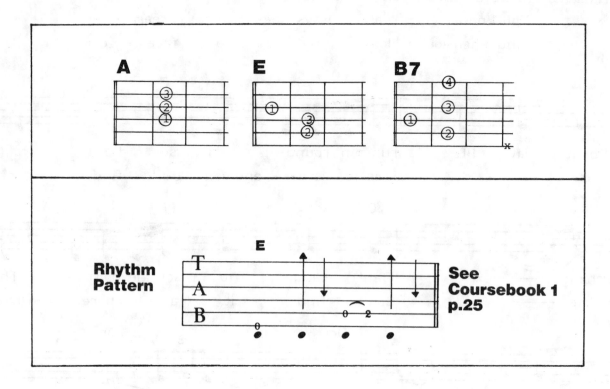

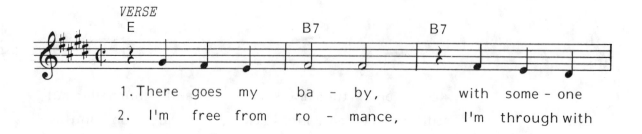

VERSE

1. There goes my ba - by, with some - one
2. I'm free from ro - mance, I'm through with

new.   She sure looks hap - py,
love.   I'm through with count - ing

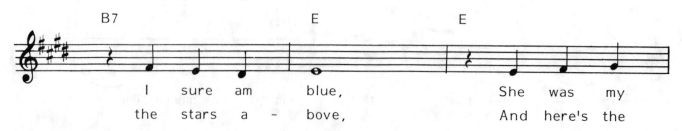

I sure am blue,   She was my
the stars a - bove,   And here's the

ba - by,   till   he   stepped   in.
rea - son   why   I'm   so   free,

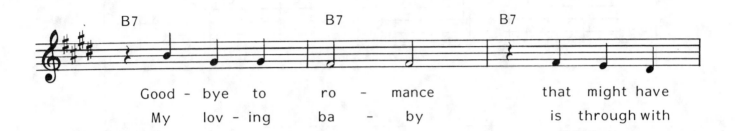

Good - bye   to   ro - mance   that   might   have
My   lov - ing   ba - by   is   through with

CHORUS

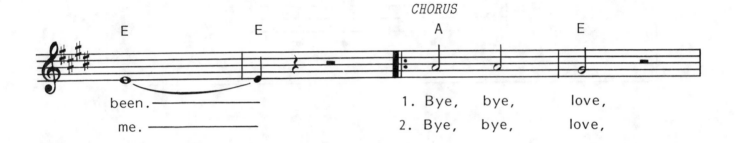

been. ————————   1. Bye,   bye,   love,
me. ————————   2. Bye,   bye,   love,

Bye,   bye,   hap - pi - ness,—   Hel - lo
Bye,   bye,   sweet ca - ress,—   Hel - lo

lone - li - ness,   I   think I'm gon - na   cry.
emp - ti - ness,   I   feel like I   could

die.   Bye   bye, my love,bye   bye.

SWEETS FOR MY SWEET

Words and Music by
DOC POMUS and MORT SHUMAN

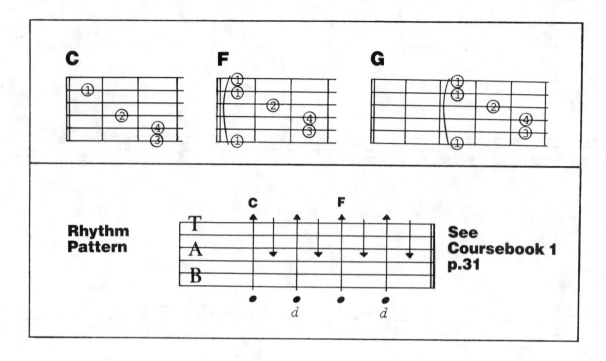

1. If you want-ed—— that star that shines so
2. If you want-ed —— a dream to keep you
3. And if you want-ed —— a love to last for -

bright-ly;—— to match the star - dust in your
smil - ing,—— I'd tell the sand - man you were
ev - er,—— darlin' I would send my love your

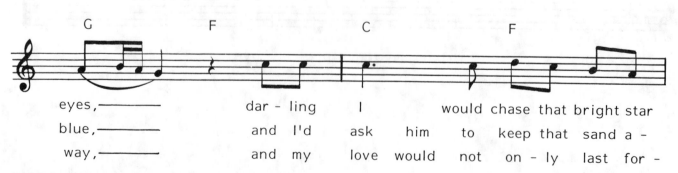

eyes,—— dar - ling I would chase that bright star
blue,—— and I'd ask him to keep that sand a -
way,—— and my love would not on - ly last for -

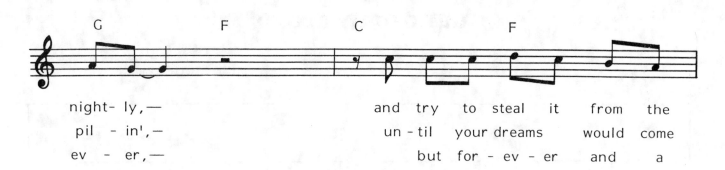

night- ly,— and try to steal it from the
pil - in',— un - til your dreams would come
ev - er,— but for - ev - er and a

CHORUS

sky.————
true.———— } And I would bring sweets for my sweet,
day.————

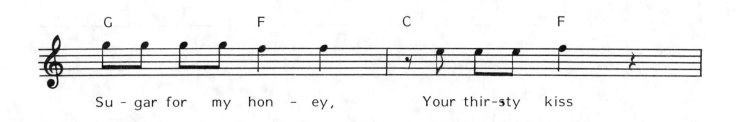

Su - gar for my hon - ey, Your thir-sty kiss

thrills me so.—— Sweets for my sweet,

su- gar for my hon- ey, I'll nev-er ev-er— let you go.—

GET OFF MY CLOUD

Words and Music by
MICK JAGGER and KEITH RICHARD

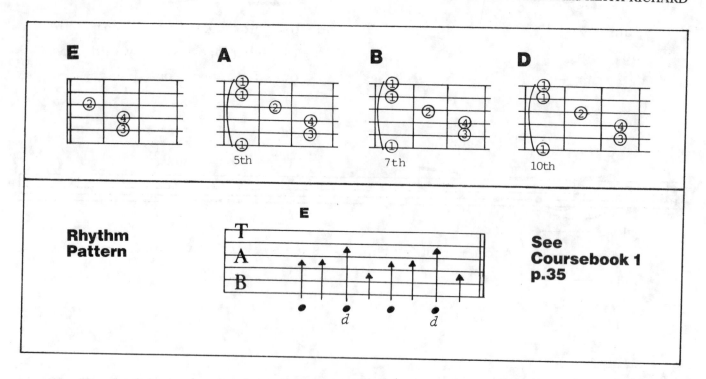

Rhythm Pattern

See Coursebook 1 p.35

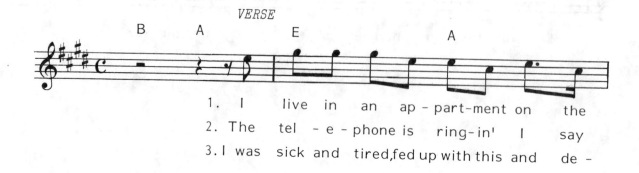

VERSE

1. I live in an ap-part-ment on the
2. The tel-e-phone is ring-in' I say
3. I was sick and tired,fed up with this and de-

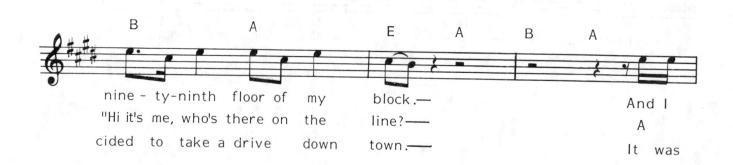

nine-ty-ninth floor of my block.— And I
"Hi it's me, who's there on the line?—— A
cided to take a drive down town.— It was

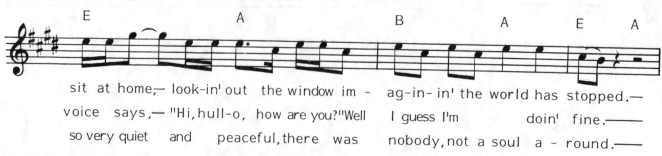

sit at home,— look-in' out the window im - ag-in-in' the world has stopped.—
voice says,— "Hi,hull-o, how are you?"Well I guess I'm doin' fine.——
so very quiet and peaceful,there was nobody,not a soul a - round.——

Westminster Music Ltd, 19/20 Poland Street, London W1V 3DD

19

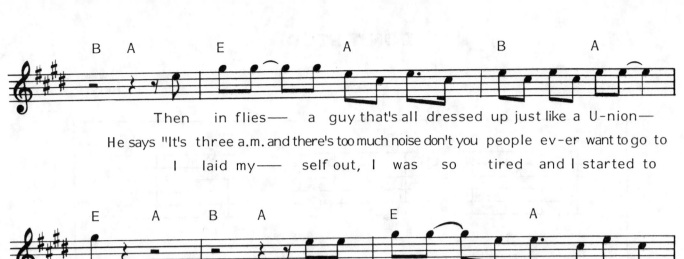

Then in flies— a guy that's all dressed up just like a U-nion—
He says "It's three a.m. and there's too much noise don't you people ev-er want to go to
I laid my— self out, I was so tired and I started to

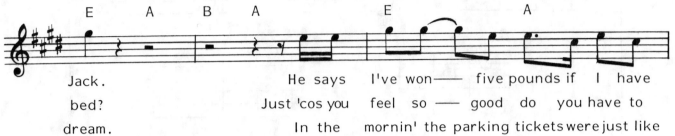

Jack. He says I've won— five pounds if I have
bed? Just 'cos you feel so — good do you have to
dream. In the mornin' the parking tickets were just like

his kind of det - er— gent pack.—
drive me out of— my head?"—   I said
flags stuck on my— wind - screen.—

CHORUS

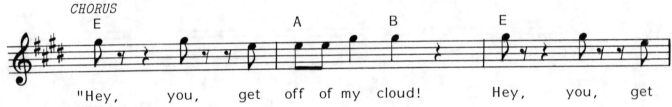

"Hey, you, get off of my cloud! Hey, you, get

off of my cloud! Hey, you, get off of my cloud!

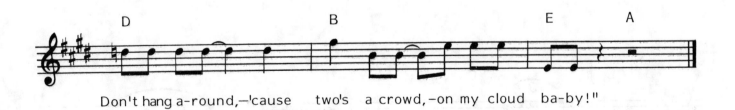

Don't hang a-round,—'cause two's a crowd,—on my cloud ba-by!"

DON'T STOP

Words and Music
by CHRISTINE McVIE

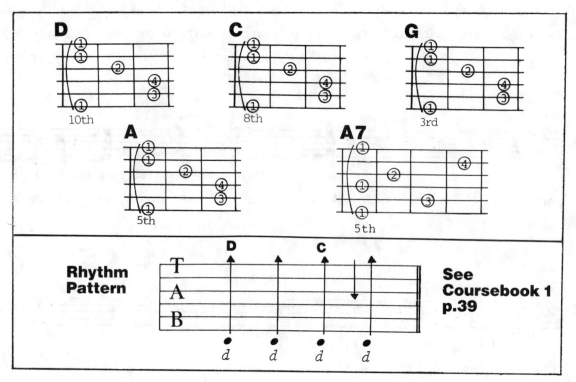

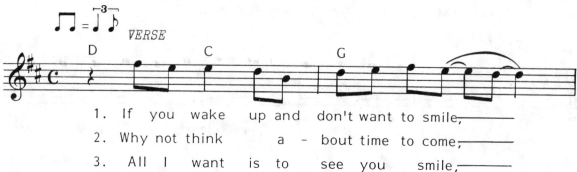

Rhythm Pattern

See Coursebook 1 p.39

1. If you wake up and don't want to smile,————
2. Why not think a - bout time to come,————
3. All I want is to see you smile,————

if it takes just a lit - tle while.
and not a - bout the things that you've done?
if it takes just a lit - tle while.

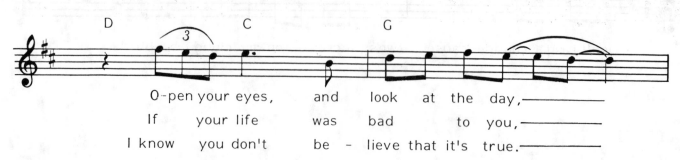

O-pen your eyes, and look at the day,————
If your life was bad to you,————
I know you don't be - lieve that it's true.————

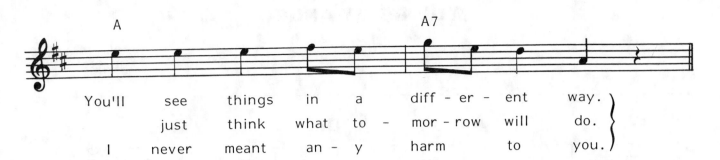

A   A7

You'll see things in a diff - er - ent way.
just think what to - mor - row will do.
I never meant an - y harm to you.

CHORUS

D   C   G

Don't stop think-in' a - bout to - mor - row.

D   C   G

Don't stop, it - 'll soon be here.——

D   C   G

It - 'll be ——————— bet - ter than be -fore.

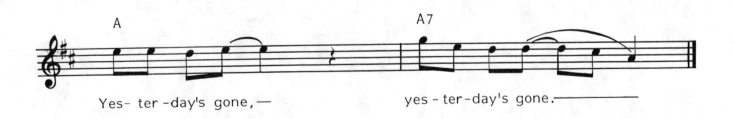

A   A7

Yes- ter -day's gone,—— yes - ter-day's gone.———————

YOU'RE MY ANGEL

Words and Music
by RUSS SHIPTON

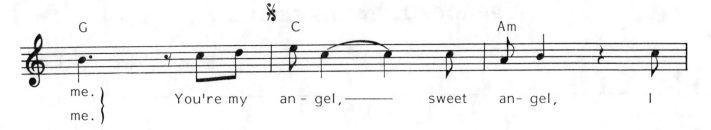

me. |
me. | You're my an-gel,——— sweet an-gel, I

pray that you'll be mine, et-er-nal-ly. Oo ee

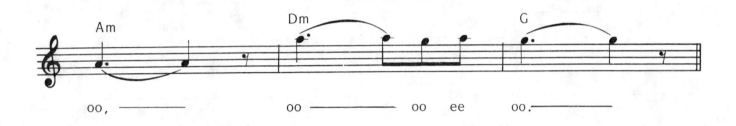

oo,——— oo ——— oo ee oo.———

MIDDLE SECTION

My an-gel, you know how I love you.

There's no one I'd place a-bove you. Please say you'll

stay with me,— for-ev-er and a day with me, my

PEACEFUL EASY FEELING

Words and Music
by JACK TEMPCHIN

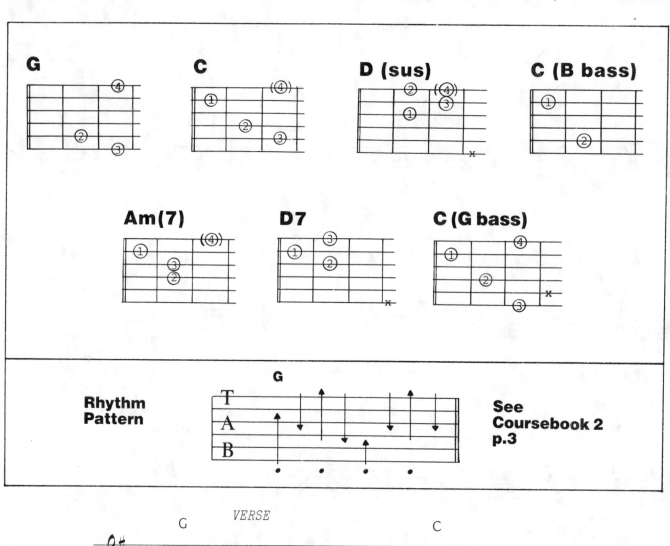

25

I wan - na sleep with you— in the des - ert— to -
Ah, but she can't take— you an - y -
But this voice keeps whis-per - ing— in my oth - er

night, with a bill - ion stars all— a -
way, you don't alread - y know how— to
ear. Tells me I may nev - er see you— a -

CHORUS

round.
go.
gain.
'Cause I got a peace-ful ——— ea— sy

feel - ing, and I know you won't let me

down, 'cause I'm al ——— read-y

stand——ing on the ground.———

ONLY SIXTEEN

Words and Music
by BARBARA CAMPBELL

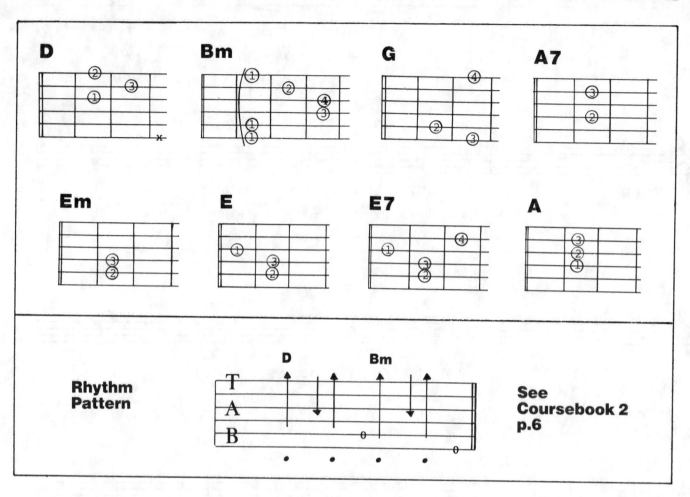

Rhythm Pattern

See Coursebook 2 p.6

VERSE

1.She was on - ly six - teen,—
2. laugh and we'd sing,— and
3. on - ly six - teen,—

on - ly six - teen,—   I loved her
do fun - ny things—   and it made our hearts
on - ly six - teen,—   with eyes that would

so,
glow,
glow,   but she was too young to

fall in love—— and I —— was too young—— to

MIDDLE SECTION

know.   2.We'd   Why did I give my

heart so fast? ——— It nev- er will hap-pen— a -

gain.   But I was a mere child of six - teen,

I've aged a year since then.   3.She was

ROCKIN' ALL OVER THE WORLD

Words and Music
by JOHN FOGERTY

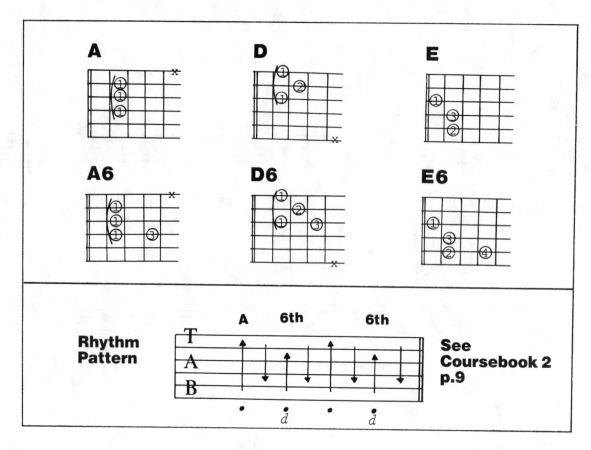

VERSES 1, 2 & 4

1. Well here we are and here we are and
2. Well gid-dy up and gid-dy up and
4. Gonna tell your mom - ma what you're

here we —— go, On and on, —— and we're
get a —— way, We're go-in' cra-y and we're
gon-na —— do, Come on a-round, get your

hit - tin' the road. ——
go - in' to - day. —— } Here we go, ————
danc - in' —— shoes. ——

© 1976 Primeval Ltd
Intersong Music Ltd, London W1Y 3FA

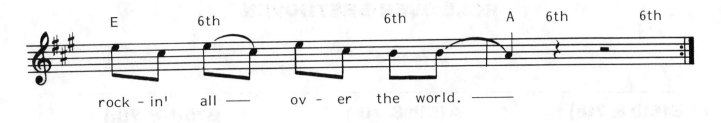

rock - in' all — ov - er the world. —

VERSE 3

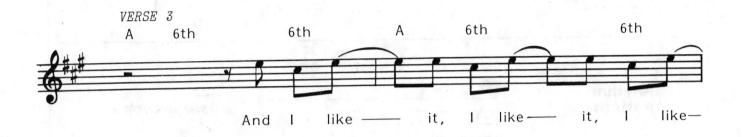

And I like — it, I like — it, I like —

— it, I like — it, I la — la la like — it. La —

— la la la. — Here we go, —

rock - in' all — ov - er the world. —

ROLL OVER BEETHOVEN

Words and Music
by CHUCK BERRY

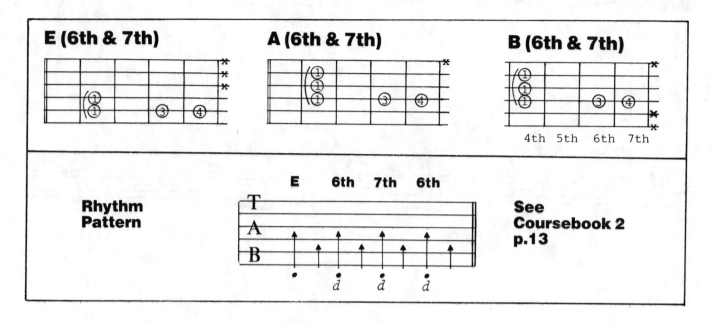

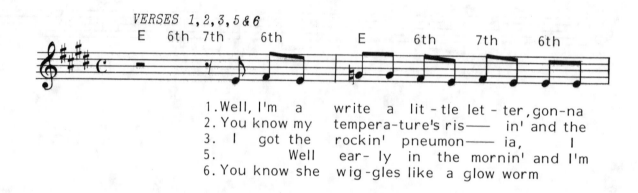

1. Well, I'm a   write a lit-tle let-ter, gon-na
2. You know my   tempera-ture's ris—— in' and the
3. I got the   rockin' pneumon—— ia,   I
5.   Well ear-ly in the mornin' and I'm
6. You know she wig-gles like a glow worm

1. mail it to my lo-cal D. J. ——   Yes, it's a
2. juke   box blow-in' a fuse, ——   My
3. used a shot of rhy-thm and blues. —   I caught the
5. giv - in' you my warnin' don't you step on my blue suede shoes.
6. dance like a spin-nin' top——   She got a

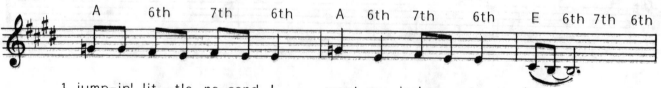

1. jump-in' lit - tle re-cord I   want my jock-ey to   play. ——
2. heart's beat-in' rhy-thm and my soul keeps a-singin' the   blues. ——
3. rol-lin' arth—— ri-tis, sittin' down at a rhythm review.
5. Hey, diddle diddle I'm playin' my fid-dle,   ain't got nothin' to
6. cra - zy part - ner, you oughta see 'em reel and rock.

Jewel Music Publishing Co Ltd, London W1Y 3FA

JAILHOUSE ROCK

Words and Music by
JERRY LEIBER and MIKE STOLLER

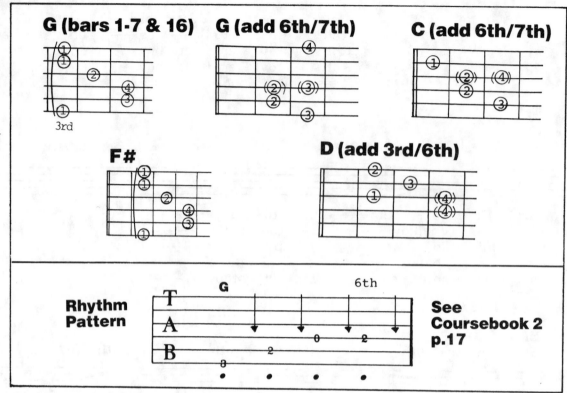

1. The war-den threw a par-ty in the
2. Spi-der Mur-phy played the ten-or
3. Num-ber for-ty sev-en said to
4. sad sack was sit-tin' on a
5. Shift-y Hen-ry said to Bugs "For

1. coun-ty jail,— the pri-son band was there and they be-
2. sax-o-phone,— Lit-tle Joe was blow-in' on the
3. num-ber three,— You're the cut-est Jail-bird I
4. block of stone,— Way ov-er in the cor-ner weep-in'
5. heav-en's sake,— No one's look-in' now's our

1. gan to wail.— The band was jump-in' and the joint be-
2. slide trom-bone.— The drum-mer boy from Ill-in-ois went
3. ev-er did see. I sure would be de-light-ed with your
4. all a-lone.— The war-den said "Hey Bud-dy, don't you
5. chance to make a break" Bug-sy turned to Shift-y and he

G   F♯   G(stop)

1. - gan   to   swing.—   You   should-'ve heard those knocked out
2. crash, boom,   bang.   The   whole   rhy- thm section was   the
3. com - pa - ny.—   Come   on   and   do   the   jail - house
4. be   no   square.   If you   can't   find   a partner, use   a
5. said   "Nix,   nix.   I   wan - na stick   a-round   a while   and

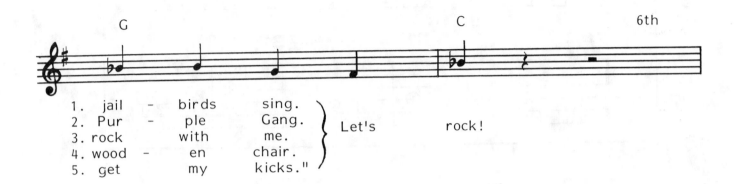

G   C   6th

1. jail - birds   sing. ⎫
2. Pur - ple   Gang. ⎬ Let's   rock!
3. rock   with   me. ⎪
4. wood - en   chair. ⎪
5. get   my   kicks." ⎭

7th   6th   G   6th   G 7th 6th

Let's   rock!   Eve - ry

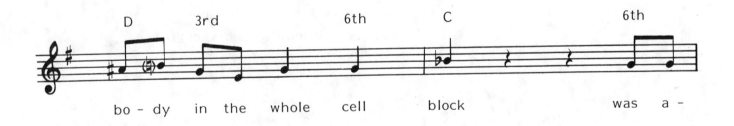

D   3rd   6th   C   6th

bo - dy   in   the   whole   cell   block   was   a-

G   C7   G   F♯

danc - ing   to   the   jail - house   rock!   (4.The)

THAT'LL BE THE DAY

Words and Music by BUDDY HOLLY,
NORMAN PETTY and JERRY ALLISON

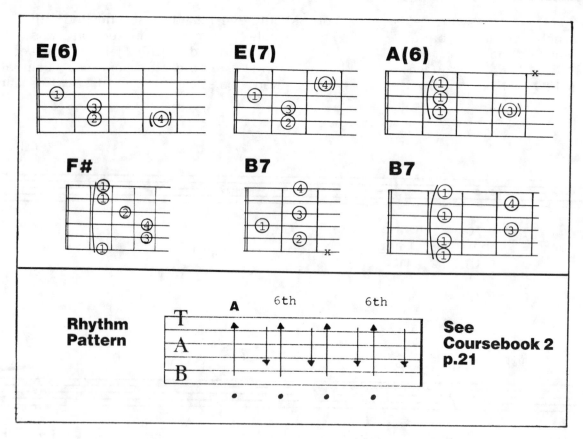

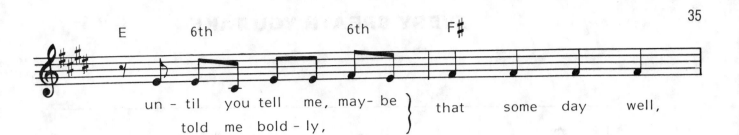

E　　　　　6th　　　　　　6th　　　　F#

un - til　you tell　me, may- be　} that　some　day　well,
told　me　bold - ly,

CHORUS

B7(pos 2)　　　　　　　　　A　　　6th　　　　6th

I'll　be　through. Well, ——　that -'ll　be　the　day,　when

A　　6th　　　　　6th　　　　E　　　6th　　　　6th

you　say— "Good-bye." Yes, ——　that - 'll　be　the　day;—　when

E　　　　　E7　　　　　　A　　　6th　　　　6th

you　make—　me　cry. Oh—　you　say you're gon- na leave,——　you

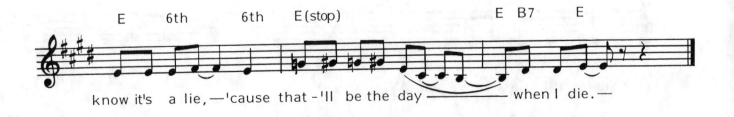

E　　6th　　　6th　E(stop)　　　　　　E　B7　　E

know it's　a　lie,—'cause that -'ll be the day ——　—— when I die. —

EVERY BREATH YOU TAKE

Words and Music
by STING

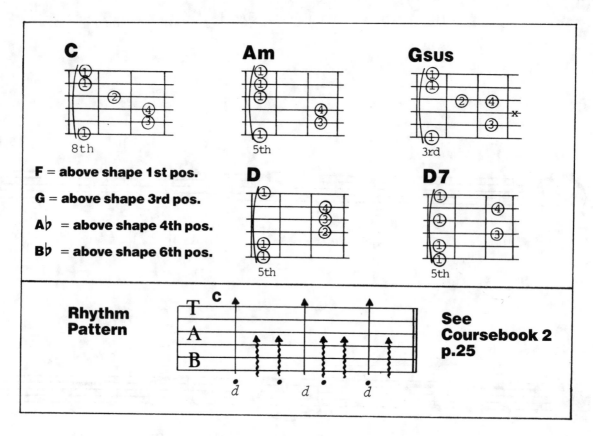

F = above shape 1st pos.

G = above shape 3rd pos.

A♭ = above shape 4th pos.

B♭ = above shape 6th pos.

Rhythm Pattern

See Coursebook 2 p.25

VERSE

1. Ev-'ry breath you— take, and ev-'ry move you—
2. Ev-'ry move you— make, and ev-'ry vow you—

make; ev-'ry bond you break; ev-'ry step you
break; ev-'ry smile you fake; ev-'ry claim you

take; I'll be watching you.
stake; I'll be watching you.

Ev-'ry sin - gle——

day, and ev-'ry word you— say;

I'M NOT IN LOVE

Words and Music by
ERIC STEWART and GRAHAM GOULDMAN

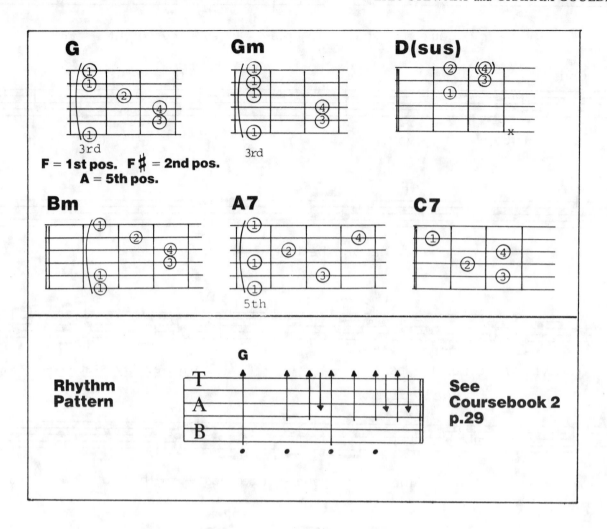

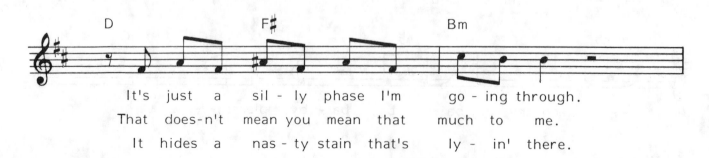

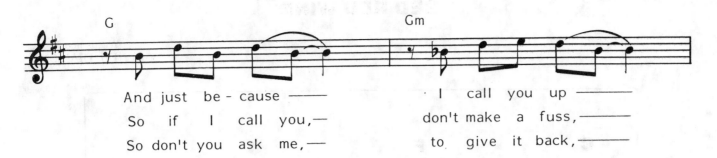

G / Gm

And just be - cause ——— I call you up ———
So if I call you,— don't make a fuss,———
So don't you ask me, — to give it back,———

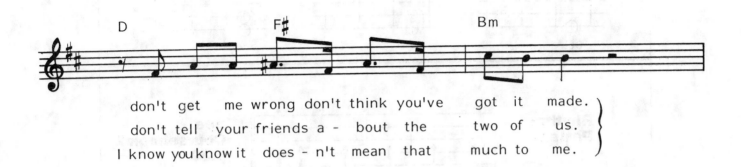

D / F# / Bm

don't get me wrong don't think you've got it made.
don't tell your friends a - bout the two of us.
I know you know it does - n't mean that much to me.

G / A A7 / D sus

I'm not in love, —— no no. It's be - cause.———

MIDDLE SECTION

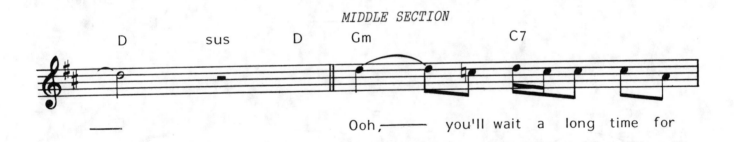

D sus D / Gm C7

— Ooh, ——— you'll wait a long time for

F / Gm C7 / Dsus D

me. ——— Ooh, —— you'll wait a long time.

RED RED WINE

Words and Music
by NEIL DIAMOND

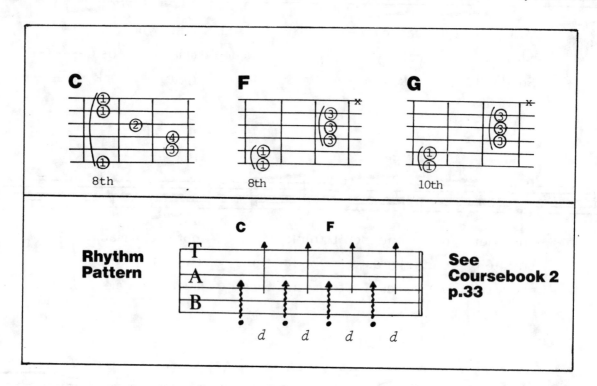

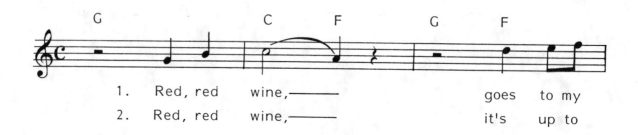

41

I'd have sworn, that with time,——

thoughts of you'd— leave my head.— I was wrong, now I

find just one thing makes me for - get. Red, red

wine,———— stay close to me.————

Don't let me be a-lone.— It's tear-in' a-

part—— my blue, blue heart.——

ALWAYS WANT YOU THERE

Words and Music
by RUSS SHIPTON

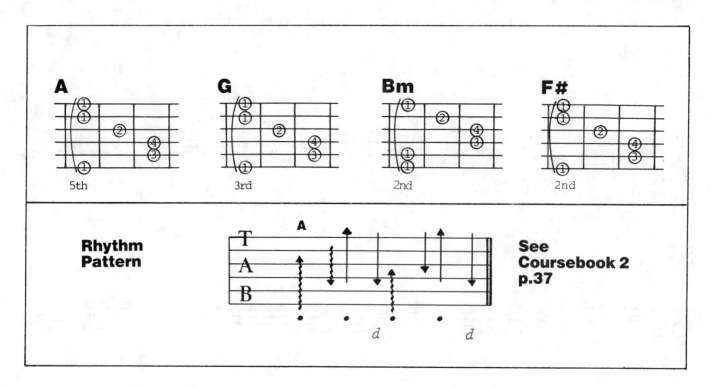

Rhythm Pattern

See Coursebook 2 p.37

CHORUS

Want you to know —— how much I love——

—— you. Want you to know —— how much I

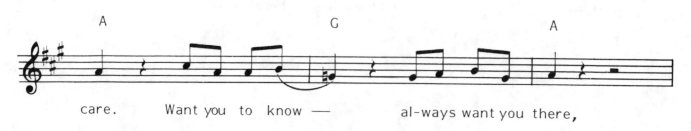

care. Want you to know — al-ways want you there,

al-ways want you there.

VERSE

1. Oh babe, the num-ber of times— I've
2. May-be I've done some run-nin' a-round— but

let you down— it's a crime— I know.
in my heart, what I've found I know.

If you walk right out of my world,— I could-n't
You're some-one so spe-cial to me. You'll

blame you girl,— but please don't go.
al-ways be,— so please don't go.

ONLY TIME WILL TELL

Words and Music
by RUSS SHIPTON

See Coursebook 2 p.42

CHORUS

C   C   F

Time will tell   if you're right or

C   C   C

wrong. You say that I'll be leav - ing you be -

G   G7   C

fore too — long. I say I'll be

C   F   C

with you till there is ice in hell.

Still you don't be - lieve me, and on- ly time will tell.

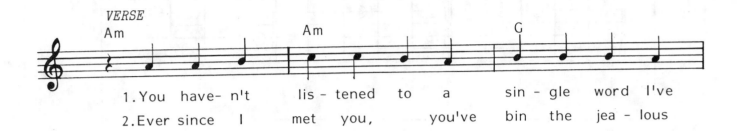

VERSE

1. You have- n't lis - tened to a sin - gle word I've
2. Ever since I met you, you've bin the jea - lous

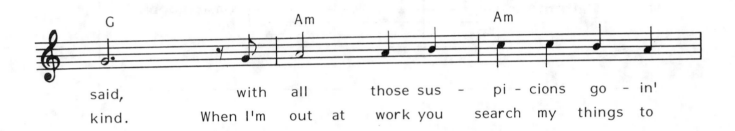

said, with all those sus - pi - cions go - in'
kind. When I'm out at work you search my things to

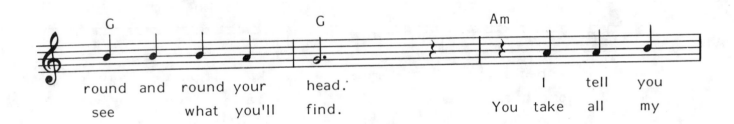

round and round your head. I tell you
see what you'll find. You take all my

black ain't white and night can't be day, but you'd
let - ters and you hold them to the light. You won - der

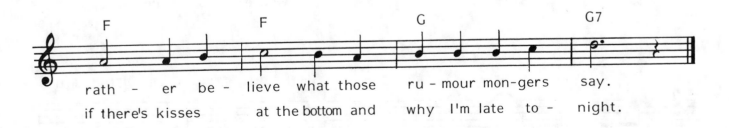

rath - er be - lieve what those ru - mour mon-gers say.
if there's kisses at the bottom and why I'm late to - night.

WHERE THE ACTION IS

Words and Music
by RUSS SHIPTON

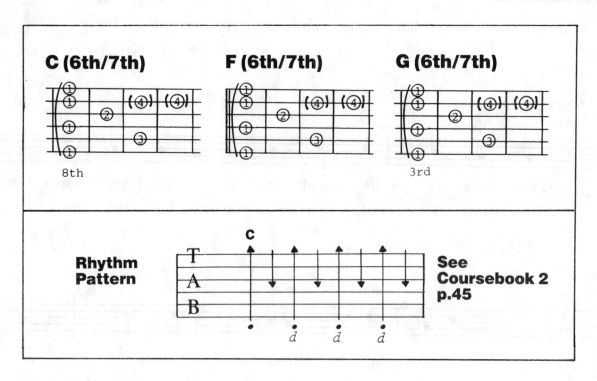

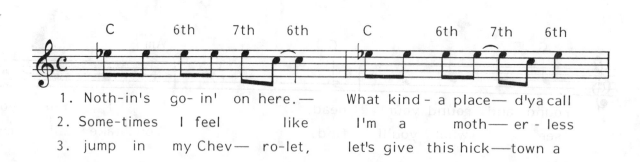

1. Noth-in's go- in' on here.— What kind- a place— d'ya call
2. Some-times I feel like I'm a moth— er - less
3. jump in my Chev— ro-let, let's give this hick—town a

this? Quiet-er than a grave-yard,— a
child. Got a tel - e - phone line———— with -
miss. Find some-where to boo - gie,

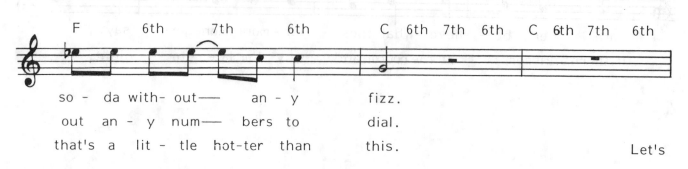

so - da with- out— an - y fizz.
out an - y num— bers to dial.
that's a lit - tle hot-ter than this.

Let's

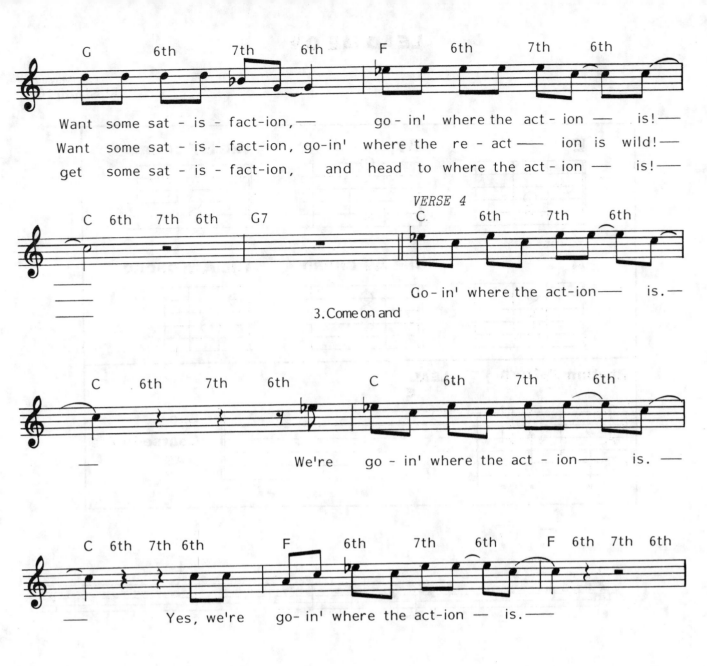

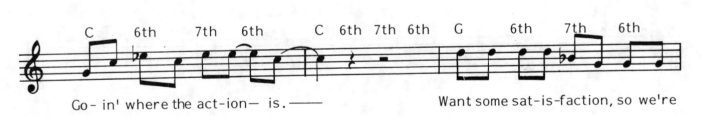

LEAD ME ON

Music by
RUSS SHIPTON

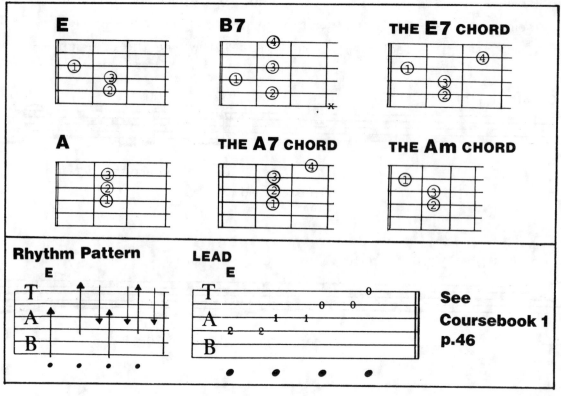

See
Coursebook 1
p.46

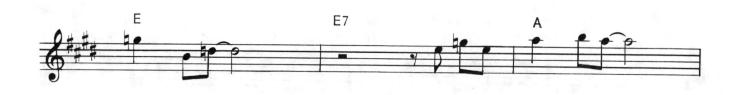

Printed in Great Britain by Loader Jackson Printers, Arlesey, Beds. 4/91